Zaner-Blos[er]
Handwriting
Middle School

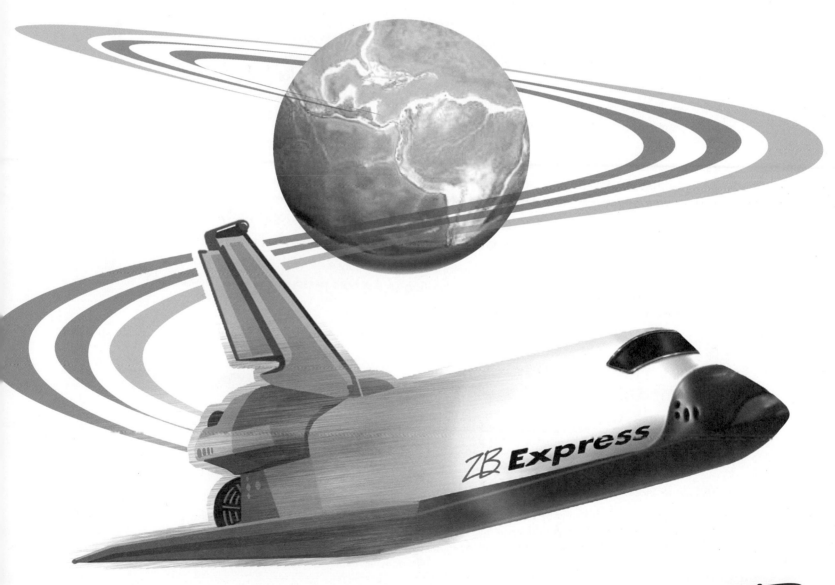

ZB Express

ZB

Note to Students

This book will help you improve your handwriting. You probably don't think about your handwriting very often. After all, you learned to write way back in elementary school. Why should you take the time to practice handwriting now that you're in middle school?

The answer is simple: You can think about your handwriting a little differently now that you are older. You realize that you write to communicate through notes and reminders to yourself, your parents, and your friends. You also write for people who will have an impact on your future, such as teachers, test evaluators, and employers. Your handwriting says a lot about you. That's why it's important to make sure your handwriting is neat and easy to read.

You can use this book to review how to write manuscript and cursive letters and to practice writing legibly. Each page features several letters and gives you space to practice the letters in words and sentences. You'll have lines with midlines for practice, and then you'll write on notebook lines, like you use in school. You'll also check yourself to see if your writing is legible. As you work through each lesson, follow these steps:

1. Complete the lessons according to the schedule your teacher gives you.

2. Plan to spend 10–15 minutes on each lesson.

3. Read through the entire lesson before you begin to write.

4. Use the Check Yourself box to honestly evaluate your work. Occasionally ask a friend or an adult to evaluate your writing.

As you grow older, you are developing your own style of writing. Use the lessons in this book to help you refine your handwriting so it is both personal to you and legible to others.

ISBN-13: 978-0-7367-5958-8

Copyright © 2009 Zaner-Bloser, Inc.

Zaner-Bloser, Inc., P.O. Box 16764, Columbus, Ohio 43216-6764
1-800-421-3018
www.zaner-bloser.com

Printed in the United States of America   10 11 12 13880 5 4 3

Table of Contents

Writing at Different Sizes

Handwriting is neat and easy to read when the reader can clearly see which letters are short (most lowercase letters) and which letters are tall (all uppercase letters and some lowercase letters).

In this book, you will notice two types of blue guidelines for your writing practice. Using both kinds of lines will help you understand the size of letters, including their proportion to each other. Writing on guidelines with four lines will allow you to focus on letter shape and size. But in the real world, you use notebook-style paper with only two guidelines—or even no lines at all. So in this book, you will also practice writing on guidelines with two llines.

Writing With Four Lines

Guidelines made up of four lines give you the most help with letter size.

Headline
Midline
Baseline
Descender Space

a t y e S g

Tall letters like t and S touch the **headline**.

Short letters like a, y, e, and g touch the dashed **midline**. They are half the height of tall letters.

All letters sit on the **baseline**.

Letters like y and g go below the baseline. Their tails, or descenders, fill the **descender space**.

The letters in a palindrome are the same forward and backward. Write the palindromes. Pay attention to the size of your letters.

Never odd or even

Rise to vote, sir.

Writing With Two Lines

Guidelines made up of two lines (just like notebook paper) require you to put your knowledge of letter size to work. If you compare the guidelines with two lines to the guidelines with four lines, you'll see that the space between the headline and the baseline is the same. But when you write on guidelines with two lines, your letters will fill only two thirds of the space, so your writing is smaller.

Imaginary Headline
Imaginary Midline
Baseline

s l j o R Y

Tall letters like l, R, and Y do not touch the top line. Instead, they stop at the imaginary **headline**.

Short letters like s, j, and o are half the height of tall letters. They stop at the imaginary **midline**.

All letters sit on the **baseline**.

Letters like j and Y have tails, or descenders, that go below the baseline. There is no special space for them. Make sure the descenders are not too long, or they will take up space for writing on the line below.

Write the palindromes. Pay attention to the size of your letters.

Was it a cat I saw?

I did, did I?

Poor Dan is in a droop.

Stella won no wallets.

Keys to Legibility for Manuscript Writing

When your papers are messy and illegible, or difficult to read, teachers or parents might say "work on your handwriting" or "pay attention to neatness." Statements like these can be confusing. What exactly can you do to improve your handwriting? Where should you start?

Good handwriting that is legible, or easy to read, doesn't happen by magic. It is the result of paying attention to four characteristics that make writing clear and consistent. These four characteristics are the **Keys to Legibility**.

1. Shape

In legible writing, each letter has a clear, unique shape. The letter **a** looks distinctly different from the letter **u,** for example. It is easy to read each letter.

To improve shape, practice writing the four basic strokes that make up all manuscript letters.

For vertical lines, pull down or push up.

For horizontal lines, slide right or slide left.

For circle lines, circle back (counterclockwise) or forward (clockwise). Make sure to close each circle.

For slant lines, slant up, slant right, or slant left.

2. Size

In legible writing, letters are in correct proportion to each other. It is easy to tell which letters are tall (all uppercase letters and some lowercase letters) and which letters are short (most lowercase letters). Short letters should be half the height of tall letters.

Write tall letters on two different kinds of writing lines.

d f h k A B

C D E F G H

Write short letters on two different kinds of writing lines.

a c g i j m

p q r s u v

3. Slant

In legible writing, all letters slant (or lean) the same way. This gives a consistent, neat appearance that is pleasing to the eye. Manuscript writing has a slant of 90°. That means it is vertical, or straight up and down.

The secret to vertical writing is the position of the paper on the desk. Position the paper as shown. Then pull strokes in the direction indicated by the arrow.

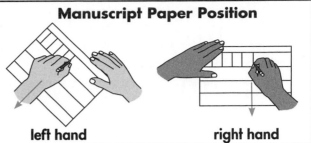

Manuscript Paper Position

left hand   right hand

Practice writing vertical manuscript letters. Position this book carefully on the desk.

The quick brown fox jumps over the lazy dog.

4. Spacing

In legible writing, spaces between letters, words, and sentences are consistent. This gives a neat appearance that is pleasing to the eye.

Between Letters: Letters should not be too close together or too far apart. Trust your eye to judge space between manuscript letters.

Between Words: Leave space for a lowercase **o** (the same size as a paper clip or the tip of your pinky finger) between words.

Between Sentences: Leave space for **oo** between sentences.

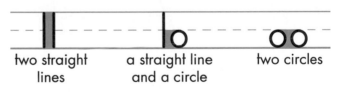

two straight lines   a straight line and a circle   two circles

Practice writing with good spacing between letters and words.

She sells seashells by the seashore.

Manuscript Pretest

Write the quotations below in your best manuscript writing. Remember the four **Keys to Legibility** explained on pages 6–7. Later, you will write the quotations again to see how you have improved.

A rainy day is the perfect time for a walk in the woods.   —Rachel Carson

Don't wait for your ship to come in; swim out to it.   —Unknown

Smooth seas do not make skillful sailors.   —African proverb

Check Yourself

❑ My letters have good **shape**.

❑ My letters are the correct **size**.

❑ The **slant** of my manuscript writing is vertical.

❑ I used good **spacing** between letters and words.

❑ My writing is easy to read.

Think About It These letters have vertical lines. They are easy to read when the lines are straight down, not slanted to the left or right. Don't forget to dot **i** and cross **t**.

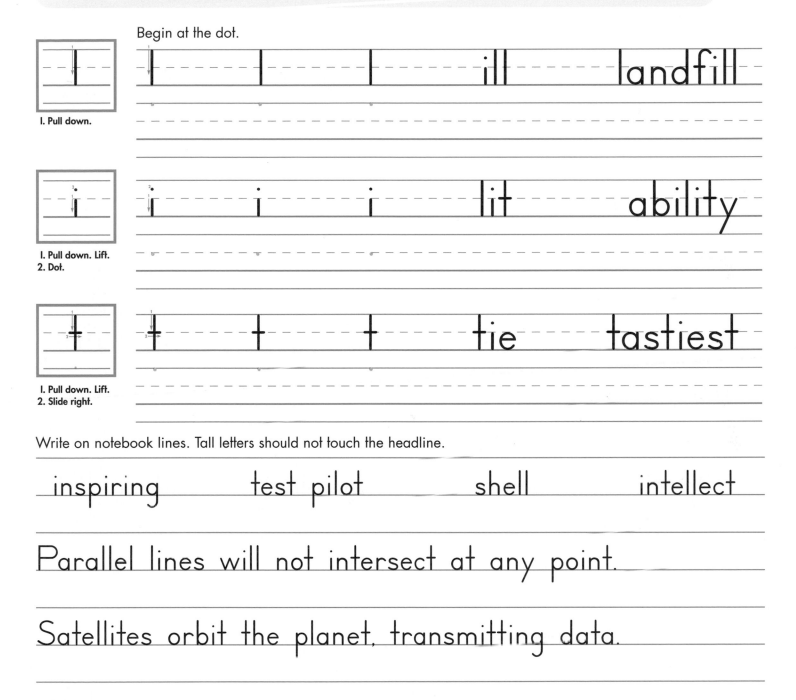

Begin at the dot.

l   l   l   l   ill   landfill

1. Pull down.

i   i   i   i   lit   ability

1. Pull down. Lift.
2. Dot.

t   t   t   t   tie   tastiest

1. Pull down. Lift.
2. Slide right.

Write on notebook lines. Tall letters should not touch the headline.

inspiring   test pilot   shell   intellect

Parallel lines will not intersect at any point.

Satellites orbit the planet, transmitting data.

☐ My letters **l, i,** and **t** have straight vertical lines.
☐ My i's have dots and my t's are crossed.
☐ My writing is easy to read.
Circle your best letter on this page.

Hint Hold your paper like this for good manuscript writing.

left hand   **right hand**

Think About It These letters begin with a counterclockwise circle. Can you see **o** inside **a** and **d**? The letter **a** inside **d**? Smooth, closed circles will make the letters easy to read.

Begin at the dot.

o   o   o   o   accord   accordion

1. Circle back.

a   a   a   a   act   bacteria

1. Circle back; push up. Pull down.

d   d   d   d   ding   pudding

1. Circle back; push up. Pull down.

Write on notebook lines. Short letters are half the height of tall letters.

adjective   armor   avocado   old-fashioned

Having your own original idea is as good as gold.

If in danger, armadillos dig into the ground.

Check Yourself

☐ My circles are closed.
☐ My letter **d** is twice as tall as my letter **a**.
☐ My writing is easy to read.
Circle your best word on this page.

Hint Having trouble getting your counterclockwise circles all the way closed? Try starting them a little lower (at about 3:00 on a clock face).

o ←   not   ⟳

Think About It These letters have counterclockwise curves. Cramped, closed curves make letters difficult to read. Make sure to keep the curves smooth and open.

Begin at the dot.

c   c   c   c   clone   cyclone

1. Circle back.

e   e   e   e   feat   feather

1. Slide right. Circle back.

f   f   f   f   for   afford

1. Curve back; pull down. Lift.
2. Slide right.

Write on notebook lines. Pages 4–5 will help you.

creampuff   fence   commander in chief

Let's meet face to face with our faithful friends.

The character slipped on a leaf for comic relief.

Check Yourself

☐ My curves are smooth and open.
☐ My letter **f** has straight vertical and horizontal lines.
☐ My writing is easy to read.
Circle your best letter on this page.

Hint For a legible letter **e**, make sure the circle back stroke touches the slide right stroke.

e   **not**   e

Think About It These letters have tails, or descenders, that drop below the baseline and curve left. For letters that are easy to read, keep curves round and open. Don't forget to dot **j**.

Begin at the dot.

j   j   j   j   just   adjust

1. Pull down; curve back. Lift.
2. Dot.

g   g   g   g   age   garage

1. Circle back; push up. Pull down; curve back.

misjudge   adjoining   goose egg

Write on notebook lines. Tall letters should not touch the headline.

jumping   joking   jaw-dropping   jug

Are you good at jumping rope or playing Mahjong?

Two adjectives are "jeweled" and "glittering."

Check Yourself

☐ My letter **j** has a straight vertical line before the curve, and a dot.
☐ My letter **g** has a round, closed circle.
☐ My writing is easy to read.
Circle your best word on this page.

Hint When writing on notebook lines, adjust spacing so that tall letters do not bump descenders on the line above.

foggy day
The next   ← **crash**

12

Manuscript Writing

Think About It On this page, you'll practice more letters with curves. Make the curves smooth and round. Keep **u** open at the top so it is not mistaken for **a**.

Begin at the dot.

u   u   u   u   pun   punctuation

I. Pull down; curve forward; push up. Pull down.

q   q   q   q   aqua   aquamarine

I. Circle back; push up. Pull down; curve forward.

s   s   s   s   salt   saltiness

I. Curve back; curve forward.

Write on notebook lines. Short letters are half the height of tall letters.

quadruplets   erasure   bureau   bouquets

The structure is made from antique brass.

Four neighbors are earthquake survivors.

Hint Think of the top of the **s** as being the top part of a circle and the bottom as the bottom part of a circle.

S   S

Think About It These letters have clockwise circles and curves. In each, the circle or curve comes after a vertical line that must be retraced. Retrace vertical lines carefully to avoid loops.

Begin at the dot.

b   b   b   b   bit   rabbit

I. Pull down.
Push up; circle
forward.

p   p   p   p   pet   appetite

I. Pull down.
Push up; circle
forward.

r   r   r   r   straw   strawberry

I. Pull down. Push
up; curve forward.

Write on notebook lines. Pages 4–5 will help you.

beekeeper   prairie   republic   problem

For my research, I read a biography of a ballplayer.

The peanut butter recipe won a blue ribbon.

Check *Yourself*

❑ My letters **b**, **p**, and **r** have straight vertical lines.
❑ My retraces are smooth, with no loops.
❑ My writing is easy to read.
Circle your best word on this page.

Hint If the circle comes after the line in a letter, retrace and make a forward circle.

b   p

Think About It These letters have clockwise curves that come after a vertical line. Can you see the letter **n** in both **m** and **h**? Retrace vertical strokes carefully before each curve.

Begin at the dot.

n   n   n   n   ton   plankton

I. Pull down. Push up; curve forward; pull down.

m   m   m   m   sum   summer

I. Pull down. Push up; curve forward; pull down. Push up; curve forward; pull down.

h   h   h   h   itch   hitch

I. Pull down. Push up; curve forward; pull down.

Write on notebook lines. Tall letters should not touch the headline.

mushroom   harmony   monarch   home run

The high-tech machine incorporates magnets.

Sample the homegrown honeydew melons.

Check Yourself

☐ My retraces are smooth, with no loops.
☐ My **n**'s are half the height of my **h**'s.
☐ My writing is easy to read.
Circle your best letter on this page.

Hint Slow down and retrace carefully for a letter **m** that is easy to read, with no loops.

m   not   m

Think About It These letters are made from slant lines. Don't write them too quickly, or they will be difficult to read. Follow the arrows to write the letter **y** correctly.

Begin at the dot.

v v v v vet velvet

1. Slant right. Slant up.

y y y y any anybody

1. Slant right. Lift.
2. Slant left.

w w w w low wallow

1. Slant right. Slant up. Slant right. Slant up.

Write on notebook lines. Short letters are half the height of tall letters.

envy   weekday   anchovy   willow

The weaver's cloth has waves of vivid yellow.

Watch out for poison ivy on the walkway.

Check Yourself

☐ My **y**'s are written with two lines.
☐ My slant lines are sharp, not rounded.
☐ My writing is easy to read.
Circle your best word on this page.

Hint Don't round slant strokes at the bottom. Letters **v**, **y**, and **w** should look like incomplete triangles.

v y w   not   v y w

Manuscript Writing

Think About It On this page you'll practice more letters with slant lines. Slow down to join strokes smoothly in **k** and **z** and to cross the two strokes that form **x**.

Begin at the dot.

x   x   x   x   sixty   sixty-six

I. Slant right. Lift.
2. Slant left.

k   k   k   k   keep   keepsake

I. Pull down. Lift.
2. Slant left. Slant
   right.

z   z   z   z   fizz   fizzled

I. Slide right. Slant
   left. Slide right.

Write on notebook lines. Pages 4–5 will help you.

zigzag   kickboxer   puzzle   chicken pox

Liz's next test is an open-book examination.

Hit the buzzer for a deluxe prize package.

Check Yourself

☐ In **k,** my slant lines touch the vertical line.
☐ My slant lines are sharp, not rounded.
☐ My writing is easy to read.
Circle your best letter on this page.

Hint Do not curve **z**. Pause after each stroke.

z   not   z

Common Problems and Corrective Strategies

Pay attention to these common problems that can make manuscript writing illegible. Use the corrective strategies to write each letter legibly.

Problem Letters slant to the left or right.

Corrective Strategy Position paper as shown on page 7. Pull vertical lines in the direction indicated. Manuscript letters should be straight up and down.

Problem Circles are incomplete.

Corrective Strategy Go all the way around to close backward circles. Try starting the circle a little lower (at about 3:00 on a clock face).

Problem Letters have loops.

Corrective Strategy Push up carefully to retrace vertical lines without a loop.

Problem Letter strokes are curved.

Corrective Strategy Pause after each stroke for sharp connections. In manuscript writing, vertical, horizontal, and slant lines are straight, not curved.

Problem Letter strokes are disconnected.

e d u k

Corrective Strategy Be sure to complete each stroke so that it helps to form the whole letter. For letters with circles or curves, push up and retrace the vertical line instead of writing a new line beside the circle or curve.

e d u k

Problem Descenders are too long or too short.

p q y j

Corrective Strategy Descenders should double the total height of their letters.

p q y j

Problem Letters are closed and cramped.

s c f v

Corrective Strategy For letters that begin with a curve back stroke, start between 1:00 and 2:00 on a clock face. Don't crowd slant strokes in letters such as **v**.

s c f v

Write the quotation legibly. Avoid common errors.

The whole purpose of education is to turn mirrors into windows.

—Sydney J. Harris

Think About It These letters begin with vertical lines written by pulling your pencil straight down. They are easy to read when they don't lean to the left or right.

Begin at the dot.

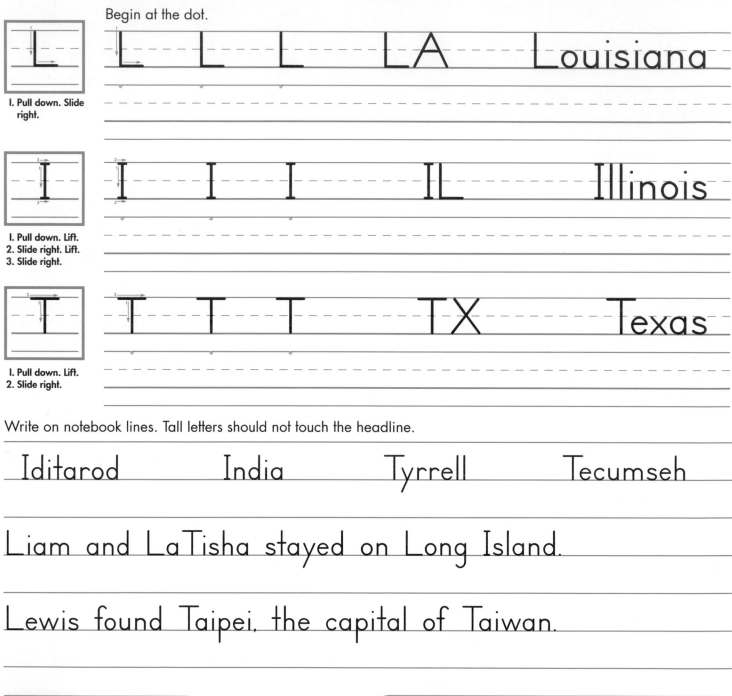

I. Pull down. Slide right.

1. Pull down. Lift.
2. Slide right. Lift.
3. Slide right.

L L L L LA Louisiana

I I I I IL Illinois

I. Pull down. Lift.
2. Slide right.

T T T T TX Texas

Write on notebook lines. Tall letters should not touch the headline.

Iditarod   India   Tyrrell   Tecumseh

Liam and LaTisha stayed on Long Island.

Lewis found Taipei, the capital of Taiwan.

Check Yourself

☐ My letters **L**, **I**, and **T** have straight vertical lines.
☐ Horizontal lines touch the vertical lines in my letters.
☐ My writing is easy to read.
Circle your best letter on this page.

Hint Write **I** with two short horizontal strokes so it is not mistaken for **l**.

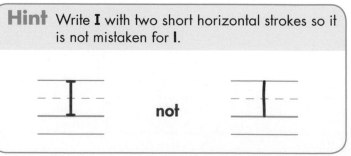

I   not   I

Think About It These letters have vertical and horizontal lines. Can you see **F** in **E**? For legible letters, write slide strokes straight across, not tilted up or down.

Begin at the dot.

E E E E   New England

1. Pull down. Lift.
2. Slide right. Lift.
3. Slide right; stop short. Lift.
4. Slide right.

F F F F   FL   Florida

1. Pull down. Lift.
2. Slide right. Lift.
3. Slide right; stop short.

H H H H   HI   Hawaii

1. Pull down. Lift.
2. Pull down. Lift.
3. Slide right.

Write on notebook lines. Short letters are half the height of tall letters.

Harry Houdini   English   Finland

Heroic Hercules slays the Hydra in this myth.

Gertrude Ederle swam the English Channel in 1926.

Check Yourself

☐ My slide strokes go straight across.
☐ In my letters **E** and **F**, the center strokes stop short.
☐ My writing is easy to read.
Circle your best word on this page.

Hint Make sure horizontal lines don't overlap.

EFH not EFH

Think About It These circle letters are easy to read when they are round and open. Slow down a little as you write them to avoid cramped oval shapes.

Begin at the dot.

O   O   O   O   OH   Ohio

1. Circle back.

Q   Q   Q   Q   Quincy, Oregon

1. Circle back. Lift.
2. Slant right.

Omaha   Quad Cities   Orlando

Write on notebook lines. Pages 4–5 will help you.

Ellen Ochoa   Okinawa   Qatar   Quebec

Oliver Quincy and Quinn O'Dell spied the ocean.

Quick Jesse Owens won four Olympic gold medals.

Check Yourself

☐ My circles are round and open.
☐ In **Q**, my slant stroke sits on the baseline.
☐ My writing is easy to read.
Circle your best letter on this page.

Hint All uppercase letters are tall letters.

Oo Qq   Oo Qq

Think About It These letters are parts of circles. They may become illegible if the curves are too closed or too open. Practice good shape. G's slide stroke shouldn't tilt up or down.

Begin at the dot.

C C C C CO Colorado

1. Circle back.

G G G G GA Georgia

1. Circle back. Slide left.

Galileo Galilei   Central College

Write on notebook lines. Tall letters should not touch the headline.

Germany   Chicago Cubs   Jane Goodall

Grover Cleveland was a U.S. president.

Gymnast Nadia Comaneci inspired young athletes.

Check Yourself

☐ In my **C** and **G**, curves are not too closed.
☐ In my **C** and **G**, curves are not too open.
☐ My writing is easy to read.
Circle your best word on this page.

Hint Use the dashed midline to help place **G**'s slide left stroke in the center. Keep this shape when writing on notebook lines, too.

G   G

Manuscript Writing

Think About It Can you see **P** in **R**? Practice the slide right/curve forward/slide left combination to make letters that are easy to read.

Begin at the dot.

P P P P P   Pikes Peak

1. Pull down. Lift.
2. Slide right; curve forward; slide left.

R R R R   Red River

1. Pull down. Lift.
2. Slide right; curve forward; slide left. Slant right.

Pocahontas   Rio Grande

Write on notebook lines. Short letters are half the height of tall letters.

Ronald Reagan   Pennsylvania   Rosa Parks

Please visit Pamela's Rocky Mountain retreat.

Rinny hurried to a rehearsal for Peter Pan.

Check Yourself

☐ Slide lines join vertical lines smoothly in my letters **P** and **R**.

☐ My letters **P** and **R** could not be mistaken for **D**.

☐ My writing is easy to read.

Circle your best letter on this page.

Hint Don't forget to include the slide strokes when writing **P** and **R**.

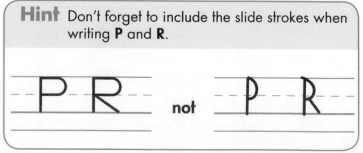

P R   not   P R

Manuscript Writing

Think About It The slide right/curve forward/slide left combination appears in these letters as well. In **D**, it extends the full height of the letter. Make vertical lines straight and tall.

Begin at the dot.

B B B B   Boston Bruins

1. Pull down. Lift.
2. Slide right; curve forward; slide left.
   Slide right; curve forward; slide left.

D D D D   DE   Delaware

1. Pull down. Lift.
2. Slide right; curve forward; slide left.

Brussels, Belgium   Discovery

Write on notebook lines. Pages 4–5 will help you.

Daniel Boone   Dorothea Dix   Bonnie Blair

Batman and Robin are the Dynamic Duo.

The BFG is by British author Roald Dahl.

Check Yourself

- ☐ I used slide lines when writing **B** and **D**.
- ☐ Slide lines do not overlap vertical lines in my letters **B** and **D**.
- ☐ My writing is easy to read.

Circle your best word on this page.

Hint In between words, there should be enough space for the letter **o**, a small paperclip, or the tip of your pinky finger.

Daniel Boone

Manuscript Writing

Think About It These letters have curved lines. They will be legible when the curves are round and open, not cramped. Practice curving smoothly in two directions for **S**.

Begin at the dot.

U   U   U   U   UT   Utah

1. Pull down; curve forward; push up.

S   S   S   S   NS   Nova Scotia

1. Curve back; curve forward.

J   J   J   J   NJ   New Jersey

1. Pull down; curve back. Lift.
2. Slide right.

Write on notebook lines. Tall letters should not touch the headline.

Jacksonville State University   John Philip Sousa

Uncle Sam is a symbol of the United States.

Shanghai's Jin Mao Building is among the tallest.

Check Yourself

❑ My letters have round, open curves.
❑ My **J** has a good slide line at the top.
❑ My writing is easy to read.
Circle your best letter on this page.

Hint Make sure your letters "sit" on the baseline.

U S J   not   U S J

Think About It Notice that each of these letters begins at the top, not on the baseline. Lift the pencil to begin the second stroke. Without the lift, letters may be cramped and illegible.

Begin at the dot.

A   A   A   A   AK   Alaska

1. Slant left. Lift.
2. Slant right. Lift.
3. Slide right.

N   N   N   N   NY   New York

1. Pull down. Lift.
2. Slant right. Push up.

M   M   M   M   MI   Michigan

1. Pull down. Lift.
2. Slant right. Slant up. Pull down.

Write on notebook lines. Short letters are half the height of tall letters.

Appalachian Mountains   Nepal   Mickey Mantle

Managua is the capital of Nicaragua.

My first stop in Maine is Acadia National Park.

Check Yourself

☐ My letters **A, N,** and **M** begin at the top.
☐ My writing has consistent slant.
☐ My writing is easy to read.
Circle your best word on this page.

Hint Push the final stroke straight up for a legible letter **N**.

N   not   N

Manuscript Writing

Think About It Letters **V** and **W** are written in one continuous stroke. They will be legible when wide open, not cramped. Notice that the top of **Y** is written with two separate lines.

Begin at the dot.

V V V V VA Virginia

1. Slant right. Slant up.

W W W W WY Wyoming

1. Slant right. Slant up. Slant right. Slant up.

Y Y Y Y Yorktown, VA

1. Slant right. Lift.
2. Slant left. Pull down straight.

Write on notebook lines. Pages 4–5 will help you.

Venezuela   Washington, D.C.   Yosemite

Vince's favorite Star Wars character is Yoda.

Water vapor can be found on the planet Venus.

Check Yourself

☐ My slant stroke letters are wide, not cramped.
☐ My spacing between letters and words is good.
☐ My writing is easy to read.
Circle your best letter on this page.

Hint For a wide, legible **Y**, join three separate strokes.

Y   not   Y

Manuscript Writing

Think About It Look at the center of each of these letters. **X** crosses in the middle. **K**'s slant lines touch the vertical line in the middle. The middle of **Z** is formed by a slant stroke.

Begin at the dot.

X   X   X   X   Xenia, OH

1. Slant right. Lift.
2. Slant left.

K   K   K   K   KS   Kansas

1. Pull down. Lift.
2. Slant left. Slant right.

Z   Z   Z   Z   Zion Canyon

1. Slide right. Slant left. Slide right.

Write on notebook lines. Tall letters should not touch the headline.

Zaire   Xerxes   Kalamazoo   Key West

Zoey read about Babe Didrikson Zaharias.

Kris hopes to compete in the X Games someday.

Check Yourself

❏ My slant line letters have good shape.
❏ My tall letters are twice the height of my short letters.
❏ My writing is easy to read.
Circle your best word on this page.

Hint For a legible **K,** slant left and touch the vertical line, pause, then slant right.

K   not   K

29

Manuscript Review

Review the **Keys to Legibility** for Manuscript Writing on pages 6–7. Then write the names of famous authors.

Madeleine L'Engle   J.K. Rowling

Wilson Rawls   Carolyn Keene

Julia Alvarez   Walter Dean Myers

Laura Ingalls Wilder   Gary Soto

W.E.B. DuBois   Ray Bradbury

Sharon Creech   Gary Paulsen

Check Yourself

☐ My letters have good **shape**.
☐ My letters are the correct **size**.
☐ The **slant** of my manuscript writing is vertical.

☐ I used good **spacing** between letters and words.
☐ My writing is easy to read.

Manuscript Posttest

Write the quotations below in your best manuscript writing. As you write, remember what you have learned by practicing your manuscript letters.

A rainy day is the perfect time for a walk in the woods. —Rachel Carson

Don't wait for your ship to come in; swim out to it. —Unknown

Smooth seas do not make skillful sailors. —African proverb

I'm not afraid of storms, I'm learning how to sail my ship. —Louisa May Alcott

Check Yourself

- ❑ My letters have good **shape**.
- ❑ My letters are the correct **size**.
- ❑ The **slant** of my manuscript writing is vertical.
- ❑ I used good **spacing** between letters and words.
- ❑ My writing is easy to read.
- ❑ Compare your writing with the writing you did for the Manuscript Pretest on page 8. Has your manuscript writing improved? Is it more legible?

Writing Numerals

Writing numerals legibly is important to your success in school and in life. You write numerals every day for tasks such as math papers, science calculations, and social studies reports. Errors and confusion can result when numerals are difficult to read. Think about how the **Keys to Legibility** apply to numerals.

> **Shape:** Each numeral should have a clear shape that is easy to identify.
>
> **Size:** Numerals should be the same height as tall letters.
>
> **Slant:** The slant of numerals should match the overall slant of your writing.
>
> **Spacing:** Numerals should have clear, consistent spacing, especially when they are in columns for a chart or math problem.

Manuscript Numerals

Use these numerals with manuscript writing. Begin at the dot.

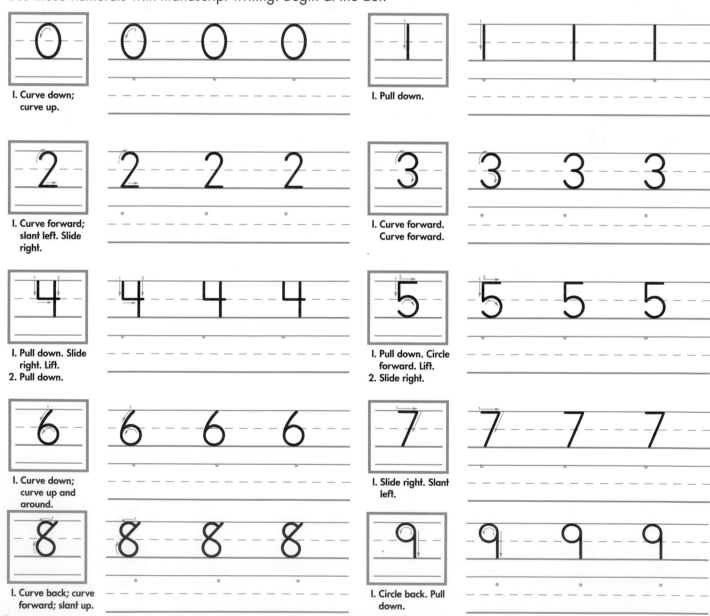

0 0 0 0
1. Curve down; curve up.

1 1 1 1
1. Pull down.

2 2 2 2
1. Curve forward; slant left. Slide right.

3 3 3 3
1. Curve forward. Curve forward.

4 4 4 4
1. Pull down. Slide right. Lift.
2. Pull down.

5 5 5 5
1. Pull down. Circle forward. Lift.
2. Slide right.

6 6 6 6
1. Curve down; curve up and around.

7 7 7 7
1. Slide right. Slant left.

8 8 8 8
1. Curve back; curve forward; slant up.

9 9 9 9
1. Circle back. Pull down.

Cursive Numerals

Use these numerals with cursive writing. Begin at the dot.

1. Downcurve;
   undercurve.

1. Slant.

1. Slant.
2. Curve forward;
   slant.
3. Curve right.

1. Slant.
2. Curve forward
   and back.
3. Curve forward
   and back.

1. Slant.
2. Slide right. Lift.
3. Slant.

1. Slant.
2. Curve forward
   and back. Lift.
3. Slide right.

1. Curve down and
   forward; loop.

1. Slant.
2. Doublecurve.
3. Slant.

1. Curve back and
   down; curve back;
   slant up.

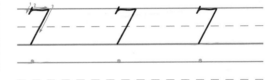
1. Downcurve;
   undercurve.
2. Slant.

Check Yourself

- [ ] My numerals have good **shape**.
- [ ] My numerals are the **size** of tall letters.
- [ ] The **slant** of my numerals is consistent.
- [ ] I used good **spacing** between numerals.
- [ ] My numerals are easy to read.

Keys to Legibility for Cursive Writing

Many students and adults prefer to use cursive writing for everyday tasks such as taking notes and making lists. You will probably use cursive for school assignments and for essays on tests. Why? Cursive handwriting is fast and flowing. When your handwriting is automatic, you can devote your full attention to the content of your writing.

Many students enjoy creating their own personal style of cursive writing. Still, it's important that your handwriting is legible. In cursive writing, each letter joins to the letter before it. Cursive letters contain loops and curves. When written quickly and carelessly, the loopy, joined strokes of cursive writing can become messy and illegible. To avoid these problems, take a look at the four **Keys to Legibility**.

1. Shape

In legible writing, each letter has a clear, unique shape. The letter *l* looks distinctly different from the letter *t*, for example. It is easy to read each letter.

To improve shape, practice writing the four basic strokes that make up all cursive letters.

For undercurve strokes, swing up.

For downcurve strokes, dive down.

For overcurve strokes, bounce up.

For slant lines, slide down.

2. Size

In legible writing, letters are in correct proportion to each other. It is easy to tell which letters are tall (all uppercase letters and some lowercase letters) and which letters are short (most lowercase letters). Short letters should be half the height of tall letters.

Write on two different kinds of writing lines.

b f h A B a e i j

D F G J K p s u x

34

3. Slant

In legible writing, all letters slant (or lean) the same way. This gives a consistent, neat appearance that is pleasing to the eye. Cursive writing has a slant of about 60°– 70°. That means it should lean slightly forward.

The secret to cursive slant is the position of the paper on the desk. Position the paper as shown. Then, pull slant lines in the direction indicated by the arrow.

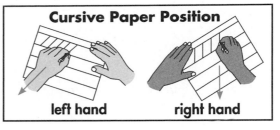

Cursive Paper Position

left hand   right hand

Practice writing cursive with consistent slant. Position this book carefully on the desk.

The quick brown fox jumps over the lazy dog.

4. Spacing

In legible writing, spaces between letters, words, and sentences are consistent. This gives a neat appearance that is pleasing to the eye.

Between Letters: Leave space for an oval between cursive letters. Joining strokes determine the spacing. Joinings should be smooth, and not too cramped or too wide.

Between Words: Leave space for a slanted line between cursive words.

Between Sentences: Leave space for uppercase O between sentences.

This is correct spacing. Look

Practice writing with good spacing between letters and words.

Lily ladles lentil soup.

Cursive Pretest

Write the brainteaser in your best cursive handwriting. Later, you will write it again to see how your cursive has improved. As you write, remember the **Keys to Legibility** explained on pages 34–35.

What can run but never walks, has a mouth but never talks, has a head but never weeps, and has a bed but never sleeps? A river!

What can run but never walks, has a mouth but never talks, has a head but never weeps, and has a bed but never sleeps? A river!

Check Yourself

☐ My letters have good **shape**.
☐ My letters are the correct **size**.
☐ My writing has consistent **slant**.

☐ I used good **spacing** between letters, words, and sentences.
☐ My writing is easy to read.

Think About It These letters begin and end with an undercurve. They have a center slant stroke. Position your paper correctly for good slant. You'll need to lift the pencil to dot **i** and cross **t**.

Begin at the dot.

i

1. Undercurve.
2. Slant; undercurve. Lift.
3. Dot.

i   i   i   ir   ig   in
i   i   i   ir   ig   in

t

1. Undercurve.
2. Slant; undercurve. Lift.
3. Slide right.

t   t   t   tw   ta   ty
t   t   t   tw   ta   ty

litter   tie   adrift   liberty
litter   tie   adrift   liberty

Write on notebook lines. Tall letters should not touch the headline.

Rival teams vied for the title.
Rival teams vied for the title
The ninth inning was exciting.
The ninth inning was exciting
With great pitching, the Tigers won.
With great pitching, the Tigers won

Check Yourself

☐ My letters **i** and **t** begin and end with an undercurve.
☐ My **i**'s have dots and my **t**'s are crossed.
☐ My writing is easy to read.
Circle your best letter on this page.

Hint Retrace strokes carefully to avoid looped letters.

i   **not**   e
t   **not**   t

Think About It These letters are written with the same strokes, but **e** is short and **l** is tall. Pay close attention to size as you write. Keep the loops in these letters open, but not too fat.

Begin at the dot.

I. Undercurve; loop back; slant; undercurve.

e e e e es ed ex

e e e es ed ex

I. Undercurve; loop back; slant; undercurve.

l l l l ll lo ly

l l l ll lo ly

yellow   vehicle   lateral

yellow   vehicle   lateral

Write on notebook lines. Short letters are half the height of tall letters.

Beside the lake, look closely.

Beside the lake, look closely.

Beetle species flourish here.

Beetle species flourish here.

The outer wings are called elytra.

The outer wings are called elytra.

Check Yourself

☐ My letters **e** and **l** end with a good undercurve stroke.
☐ My letter **l** is twice as tall as my letter **e**.
☐ My writing is easy to read.
Circle your best word on this page.

Hint Keep loops open for letters that are easy to read.

e l **not** *e l*

38

Think About It Begin these letters with an undercurve/loop back/slant combination. Pause before continuing with the overcurve stroke. For a legible letter, be sure to close **k**.

Begin at the dot.

1. Undercurve; loop back; slant.
2. Overcurve; slant; undercurve.

h   h   h   h   hu   ha   hy

h   h   h   hu   ha   hy

1. Undercurve; loop back; slant.
2. Overcurve; curve forward; curve under.
3. Slant right; undercurve.

k   k   k   k   kh   ko   kn

k   k   k   kh   ko   kn

backache   hammock

backache   hammock

Write on notebook lines. Pages 4–5 will help you.

Try hard to be kind to others.

Try hard to be kind to others

Give a hearty handshake.

Give a hearty handshake.

Make use of your handkerchief.

Make use of your handkerchief.

Check Yourself

❑ My loops are closed in **h** and **k**.
❑ My writing has consistent slant.
❑ My writing is easy to read.
Circle your best letter on this page.

Hint End **h** and **k** with a full undercurve stroke. This will ensure good spacing between letters.

ha   kh

Swing undercurves wide to begin the next letter.

Think About It These letters have loops that descend below the baseline. Don't make them dip too low, or there won't be space to write on the line below. Close your loops for easy-to-read letters.

Begin at the dot.

1. Undercurve; loop back; slant; loop forward.
2. Undercurve.

f   f   f   f   ft   fa   fy
f   f   f   ft   fa   fy

1. Undercurve.
2. Slant; loop back; overcurve; curve back.
3. Undercurve.

p   p   p   ph   po   pn
p   p   pe   ph   po   pn

flip-flop   fill-up   puff
flip flop   fill-up   puff

Write on notebook lines. Tall letters should not touch the headline.

My favorite hobby is photography.
My favorite hobby is photography
I took pictures on our field trip.
I took pictures on our field trip
The photos show friendship and fun.
The photos show friendship and fun

Check Yourself

☐ My loops are closed in **f** and **p**.

☐ My letters **f** and **p** begin with an undercurve.

☐ My writing is easy to read.

Circle your best word on this page.

Hint When writing on notebook lines, adjust spacing so that tall letters do not bump descenders from the line above.

crash → *flip-flop*
        The sky

Cursive Writing

Begin at the dot.

r *r* *r* *ru* *rd* *rm*

1. Undercurve.
2. Slant right.
3. Slant; undercurve.

r *r* *r* *ru* *rd* *rm*

s *s* *s* *ss* *sq* *sn*

1. Undercurve.
2. Retrace; curve down and back.
3. Undercurve.

s *s* *s* *ss* *sq* *sn*

scarecrow   reassure   stare

scarecrow   reassure   stare

Write on notebook lines. Short letters are half the height of tall letters.

The country's leaders met in secret.

The country's leaders met in secret

Officials argued over strategies.

Officials argued over strategies

A secretary recorded the decision.

A secretary recorded the decision

Think About It Notice that the letter **x** begins with an overcurve stroke (see page 34). Make **x** wide enough to allow the final slant stroke. You will need to lift your pencil to add it.

Begin at the dot.

u u u u ut ug un

u u u ut ug un

1. Undercurve.
2. Slant; undercurve.
3. Slant; undercurve.

x x x x xi xc xy

x x x xi xc xy

1. Overcurve; slant; undercurve. Lift.
2. Slant.

exhaust   box lunch

exhaust   box lunch

Write on notebook lines. Pages 4–5 will help you.

This excerpt is about the galaxy.
This excerpt is about the galaxy
Some of the facts are unexpected.
Some of the facts are unexpected
Humans should explore the universe.
Humans should explore the universe.

Check Yourself

❑ My letter **u** has good slant.
❑ My letter **x** is wide enough and is crossed with a slant stroke.
❑ My writing is easy to read.
Circle your best word on this page.

Hint For a legible letter that has good slant, pause after the first two undercurves in **u**.

Pause.   Pause.

u

Cursive Writing

n   n   n   n   nt   nd   nn

n   n   n   nt   nd   nn

1. Overcurve; slant.
2. Overcurve; slant; undercurve.

m   m   m   m   mu   ma   mm

m   m   m   mu   ma   mm

1. Overcurve; slant.
2. Overcurve; slant.
3. Overcurve; slant; undercurve.

acronym   anonymous

acronym   anonymous

Write on notebook lines. Tall letters should not touch the headline.

Nan's minestrone is yummy.

Nan's minestrone is yummy.

She adds tomatoes and zucchini.

She adds tomatoes and zucchini.

The final ingredient is macaroni.

The final ingredient is macaroni.

Check Yourself

☐ My **n** has two "humps," and my **m** has three.

☐ My letters **n** and **m** have no loops.

☐ My writing is easy to read.

Circle your best letter on this page.

Hint For good slant, position your paper as shown. Pull slant strokes in the direction indicated.

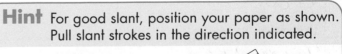

left hand   **right hand**

Cursive Writing

Think About It These letters have the same strokes, but **a** is short and **d** is tall. Pay attention to size so they are not mistaken for each other. Notice that they begin with a downcurve.

Begin at the dot.

a   *a   a   a   ap   ag   ax*

a   a   a   ap   ag   ax

1. Downcurve; undercurve.
2. Slant; undercurve.

d   *d   d   d   du   da   dy*

d   d   d   du   da   dy

1. Downcurve; undercurve.
2. Slant; undercurve.

cheddar   address   dollar

cheddar   address   dollar

Write on notebook lines. Short letters are half the height of tall letters.

See the Outstanding Student Award?

See the Outstanding Student Award?

It is for academic achievement.

It is for academic achievement.

It also rewards a good attitude.

It also rewards a good attitude

Check Yourself

☐ My letters **a** and **d** begin with a downcurve.

☐ My **a**'s and **d**'s are closed at the top.

☐ My writing is easy to read.

Circle your best word on this page.

Hint The letters **a** and **d** contain the letter **i** without the dot.

a d

Think About It Look at these letters. Though both begin with a downcurve stroke, **c** remains open while **q** is closed. Both letters end with an undercurve stroke.

Begin at the dot.

c
1. Downcurve; undercurve.

c   c   c   cr   ca   cy

c   c   c   cr   ca   cy

q
1. Downcurve; undercurve.
2. Slant; loop forward.
3. Undercurve.

q   q   q   qu   quack

q   q   q   qu   quack

qualification   accent

qualification   accent

Write on notebook lines. Pages 4–5 will help you.

The quarterback aims for accuracy.

The quarterback aims for accuracy

This exercise is for the quadriceps.

This exercise is for the quadriceps

After practice, quench your thirst.

After practice quench your thirst

Hint Write **c** carefully so it is not confused with **e** or **o**.

c   **not**   e   **or**   o

Undercurve Joinings

All the cursive letters you have practiced so far end with an undercurve stroke. When you connect these letters to other cursive letters, you are writing an undercurve joining. Take a look at these tips for undercurve joinings.

Undercurve-to-Undercurve
Swing wide to form undercurve of the next letter.

el

Keep open.

Undercurve-to-Downcurve
Swing up and over to form top of downcurve letter.

ra

Keep open.

Undercurve-to-Overcurve
Swing up and over. Undercurve turns into overcurve.

ty

Keep open.

All the letters in this phrase end with an undercurve. Combine the letters to form new words and write them on the lines below. How many new words can you make?

ice cream stand

create   race

name   steam

meat   team

need

nice

mice

mean

rice

Write each joining under the correct heading. Beside each joining, write a word that includes that joining. You may use a dictionary to help you.

fa   ex   ki   lp   iv   ho
py   ig   ew   th   tn   eq

Undercurve-to-Undercurve Joinings

Undercurve-to-Downcurve Joinings

Undercurve-to-Overcurve Joinings

Check *Yourself*

❏ My letters and joining strokes have good **shape**.

❏ My letters are the correct **size**.

❏ My writing has consistent **slant**.

❏ Good joining strokes make good **spacing** between my letters.

❏ My writing is easy to read.

Think About It These letters have loops below the baseline. For legibility, make the loops long enough, but not so long that they will interfere with writing below. Notice that these letters end with an overcurve.

Begin at the dot.

g

1. Downcurve; undercurve.
2. Slant; loop back; overcurve.

g   g   g   gr   gg   gn
g   g   g   gr   gg   gn

j

1. Undercurve.
2. Slant; loop back; overcurve. Lift.
3. Dot.

j   j   j   je   jo   jy
j   j   j   je   jo   jy

bungee   *jogging*   *jargon*
bungee   *jogging*   *jargon*

Write on notebook lines. Tall letters should not touch the headline.

A jet brought us to the jungle.
A jet brought us to the jungle
Our subject of study is geology.
Our subject of study is geology
We glimpsed a prowling jaguar.
We glimpsed a prowling jaguar

Check Yourself

☐ My letters **g** and **j** end with full overcurves.
☐ My letter **j** has a dot.
☐ My writing is easy to read.
Circle your best word on this page.

Hint Don't stop the overcurve ending short. Swing it all the way up to the middle of the writing space.

j   not   *j*

48

Think About It Look at these letters. They start on the baseline. They begin and end with an overcurve that bounces up to the center of the writing space. Practice writing full, complete overcurves.

Begin at the dot.

y

1. Overcurve; slant; undercurve.
2. Slant; loop back; overcurve.

y   *y*   *y*   *yl*   *yo*   *ym*

y   *y*   *y*   *yl*   *yo*   *ym*

z

1. Overcurve; slant.
2. Overcurve; curve down; loop; overcurve.

z   *z*   *z*   *zi*   *za*   *zz*

z   *z*   *z*   *zi*   *za*   *zz*

frenzy   *zero*   *gravity*

frenzy   *zero*   *gravity*

Write on notebook lines. Short letters are half the height of tall letters.

"Breeze" and "zephyr" are synonyms.
"Breeze" and "zephyr" are synonyms.
"Lazy" and "zesty" are antonyms.
"Lazy and "zesty" are antonyms
What are "crazy" and "zany"?
What are "crazy" and "zany"?

Check Yourself

☐ My letters **y** and **z** begin on the baseline.
☐ My writing has good spacing between letters.
☐ My writing is easy to read.
Circle your best letter on this page.

Hint There should be space for an oval between letters. Wide, well-formed joining strokes allow good letter spacing.

ym

Overcurve Joinings

You have practiced letters that end with an overcurve stroke. When you connect these letters to other cursive letters, you are writing an overcurve joining. Take a look at these tips for overcurve joinings.

Overcurve-to-Undercurve
Swing low. Overcurve turns into undercurve.

je

Keep open.

Overcurve-to-Downcurve
Swing wide to form top of downcurve letter.

ga

Keep open.

Overcurve-to-Overcurve
Swing up. Overcurve ending turns into overcurve beginning.

zy

Keep open.

---

yacht   jumbo   gauge   juggle   zygote   yield   rhyme

Write the word that matches each clue. Use cursive writing. Pay close attention to overcurve joinings.

measuring device	*gauge*
fertilized egg	*zygote zygote*
give way	*yield yield yield*
pleasure boat	*yacht yacht yacht*
nursery	*nursery nursery rhyme*
giant	*jumbo jumbo*
party trick	*juggle juggle*

Write each joining under the correct heading. Beside each joining, write a word that includes that joining. You may use a dictionary to help you.

go zz ji ze gn ya
zo ym ja zy yi gl

Overcurve-to-Undercurve Joinings

Overcurve-to-Downcurve Joinings

Overcurve-to-Overcurve Joinings

Think About It These letters have different beginnings, but their endings are the same. The very short stroke at the end is called a checkstroke. Checkstrokes are like tow hooks that link letters.

Begin at the dot.

b

1. Undercurve; loop back; slant; undercurve.
2. Checkstroke.

b   b   b   br   ba   by

b   b   b   br   ba   by

o

1. Downcurve; undercurve.
2. Checkstroke.

o   o   o   os   od   oz

o   o   o   os   od   oz

lobby   obvious   adorable

lobby   obvious   adorable

Write on notebook lines. Pages 4–5 will help you.

Do you have a baby-sitting job?

Do you have a baby-sitting job?

You may bring balloons to toss.

You may bring balloons to toss

Read a storybook before bed.

Read a storybook before bed

Check Yourself

☐ My letters **b** and **o** end with good checkstrokes.
☐ My **b** is twice as tall as my **o**.
☐ My writing is easy to read.
Circle your best word on this page.

Hint The two checkstroke joinings shown below are tricky to write. They change the shape of **r** and **s**. Deepen the checkstroke before beginning the undercurve of the second letter.

br   os

Cursive Writing

Begin at the dot.

1. Overcurve; slant; undercurve.
2. Checkstroke.

v v v vu va vv

v v v vu va vv

1. Undercurve.
2. Slant; undercurve.
3. Slant; undercurve.
4. Checkstroke.

w w w we wo wy

w w w we wo wy

vowel   weevil   waiver

vowel   weevil   waiver

Write on notebook lines. Tall letters should not touch the headline.

Viv viewed the river level.

Viv viewed the river level.

The water was very low.

The water was very low

Two feet is the November average.

Two feet is the November average.

53

Checkstroke Joinings

You have practiced cursive letters that end with a checkstroke. Joining a letter that ends in a checkstroke to the letter that follows can be tricky. Take a look at these tips for checkstroke joinings.

Checkstroke-to-Undercurve

Swing right. Deepen the checkstroke a little. It takes the place of **i**'s undercurve.

wi

Pause and retrace slightly before swinging right.

Checkstroke-to-Downcurve

Swing wide. Joining stroke forms top of downcurve letter.

oc

Pause and retrace slightly before swinging right.

Checkstroke-to-Overcurve

Pause and retrace slightly before swinging right.

by

Swing into overcurve.

biology	bouquet	opinion	vibration
oblique	boycott	ozone	withdrawal
vandal	voyage	wither	worthwhile

Write these words in alphabetical order. Use cursive writing. Pay close attention to checkstroke joinings.

biology

oblique

vandal

bouquet

boycott

voyage

opinion

ozone

wither

vibration

withdrawls

worthwhile

Write each joining under the correct heading. Beside each joining, write a word that includes that joining. You may use a dictionary to help you.

vi   om   vo   ws   by   wn
oo   br   ou   ba   ov   od

Checkstroke-to-Undercurve Joinings

Checkstroke-to-Downcurve Joinings

Checkstroke-to-Overcurve Joinings

Check *Yourself*

☐ My letters and joining strokes have good **shape**.

☐ My letters are the correct **size**.

☐ My writing has consistent **slant**.

☐ Good joining strokes make good **spacing** between my letters.

☐ My writing is easy to read.

Focus on...

Common Problems and Corrective Strategies

Pay attention to these common problems that can make cursive writing illegible. Use the corrective strategies to write each letter legibly.

Problem Letters have unnecessary loops.

Corrective Strategy Pause at the top of the letter before the retrace. For letters such as **m,** pause at the bottom. Retrace lines carefully.

Problem Necessary loops are cramped or closed entirely.

Corrective Strategy Make entry stroke wide to allow for the loop to follow.

Problem Slant is poor.

Corrective Strategy Position paper correctly for cursive writing, as shown on page 35. Pull slant strokes in the direction indicated. To check the slant of your writing, draw faint pencil lines through several slant strokes. The lines should be parallel.

Problem Curves are not closed. Letters are open and illegible.

Corrective Strategy Complete each stroke to close curves. Make deep curves that will connect well.

Problem Undercurve strokes are poorly written.

u o a r

Corrective Strategy Make undercurve strokes deep and wide. Swing up to the right.

u c a r

u c a r

Problem Checkstrokes are poorly written.

w h a n

Corrective Strategy For legible checkstrokes, retrace slightly and curve right. Keep checkstrokes near the center of the writing space.

w b o v

w b o v

Problem Overcurve strokes are poorly written.

j g h n

Corrective Strategy Make the overcurve stroke in a smooth, continuous motion. Do not change direction midstroke. Overcurve endings, as in **j**, should cross at the baseline, not above or below it.

j g h n

j g h n

Write the quotation legibly. Avoid common errors.

A friend accepts us as we are yet helps us to be what we should. —Anonymous

A friend accepts us as we are yet helps us to be what we should. — Anonymous

Think About It Look at these letters. They include an oval-like shape made from a tall downcurve followed by an undercurve. **C** begins with a tiny slant stroke.

Begin at the dot. **A** and **C** join the letter that follows.

A

1. Downcurve; undercurve.
2. Slant; undercurve.

A   A   At   Ad   Am

A   A   At   Ad   Am

C

1. Slant.
2. Downcurve; undercurve.

C   C   Cr   Ca   Cy

C   C   Cr   Ca   Cy

Atlantic   Churchill   Aesop

Atlantic   Churchill   Aesop

Write on notebook lines. Tall letters should not touch the headline.

Anita Cook attends Central Academy.
Chemistry and American history are
Anita's favorite subjects.

Anita Cook attends Central Academy
Chemistry and American history are
Anita's favorite subjects

Check *Yourself*

❏ My letter **A** has a good retrace.
❏ My letter **C** has an open curve.
❏ My writing is easy to read.
Circle your best letter on this page.

Hint Pause before the retrace in **A**. In **C**, pause after the slant stroke.

a ← Pause   *C* ← Pause

Cursive Writing

Think About It These letters each contain a loop. For letters that are easy to read, keep the loops small but open. You will need to pick up your pencil to write letters that follow **O**.

Begin at the dot. **E** joins the letter that follows. **O** does not.

E   *E*   *E*   *El*   *Ed*   *En*

E   *E*   *El*   *Ed*   *En*

1. Slant.
2. Downcurve;
   loop; downcurve;
   undercurve.

O   *O*   *Oct.*   *October*

O   *O*   *Oct*   *October*

1. Downcurve;
   undercurve; loop;
   curve right.

Egypt   *Osceola*   *Einstein*

Egypt   *Osceola*   *Einstein*

Write on notebook lines. Short letters are half the height of tall letters.

Oxford University is in England.
Oxford is one of the oldest English-
language universities in the world.
Oxford University is in England.
Oxford is one of the oldest English
language universities in the world.

Check Yourself

☐ My letters **E** and **O** have open loops.
☐ My writing has consistent slant.
☐ My writing is easy to read.
Circle your best word on this page.

Hint For consistent slant, position your paper as shown on page 35.

E   **not**   *E*

Think About It Look at the letter **I**. It begins just below the baseline with a tall overcurve. Don't make **I** too skinny or too fat. For legibility, keep the loop open.

Begin at the dot. Joining **I** to the letter that follows is optional.

I I I I Iceland

I I I Iceland

1. Overcurve; curve down and up.
2. Retrace; curve right.

Istanbul Ireland Idaho

Istanbul Ireland Idaho

Inca Indonesia Irving

Inca Indonesia Irving

Write on notebook lines. Pages 4–5 will help you.

Is your cousin Ian from Indianapolis, Indiana? I was there with
Isabel on Independence Day.

Is your cousin Ian from Indianapolis
Indiana? I was there with
Isabel on Independence Day

Check Yourself

☐ My letter **I** has an open loop.
☐ My tall letters are twice the height of my short letters.
☐ My writing is easy to read.
Circle your best letter on this page.

Hint Do you prefer to join **I** to other letters, or not? It's up to you.

Is Is

Think About It These letters have tall curves that begin on the baseline (**Q**) or just below it (**J**). It takes practice to write the curves well, especially to go all the way around to close **Q**. Practice at a large size on scrap paper.

Begin at the dot. **J** joins the letter that follows. **Q** does not.

J

1. Overcurve; slant; loop back; overcurve.

J J Ju Jo Jy
J J Ju Jo Jy

Q

1. Curve back; overcurve; curve down; retrace; curve forward; curve under.

Q Q Q Quapaw
Q Q Q Quapaw

January Quinn Jupiter
January Quinn Jupiter

Write on notebook lines. Tall letters should not touch the headline.

Qadir lives in the Middle Eastern country Qatar. Johari lives in Jordan, a nearby nation.

Qadir lives in the Middle Eastern country Qatar. Johari lives in Jordan, a nearby nation

Check Yourself

☐ My **J** begins just below the baseline.
☐ My **Q** has a good loop.
☐ My writing is easy to read.
Circle your best word on this page.

Hint Swing wide to make letters that are open and easy to read.

J Q   not   *J Q*

61

Think About It These letters begin with a curve forward, slant stroke that resembles a candy cane. The humps that come after are shorter in height. Swing wide to end **N** and **M** at the midline.

Begin at the dot. **N** and **M** join the letter that follows.

1. Curve forward; slant.
2. Overcurve; slant; undercurve.

N   N   Ne   No   Ny
N   N   Ne   No   Ny

1. Curve forward; slant.
2. Overcurve; slant.
3. Overcurve; slant; undercurve.

M   M   Mi   Mo   My
M   M   Mi   Mo   My

New Mexico   Mrs.   Montana
New Mexico   Mrs.   Montana

Write on notebook lines. Short letters are half the height of tall letters.

Nelson Mandela fought apartheid
in South Africa. Mandela won the
Nobel Peace Prize in 1993.
Nelson Mandela fought apartheid
in South Africa. Mandela won the
Nobel Peace Prize in 1993.

Check Yourself

☐ My overcurves are rounded in **N** and **M**.
☐ My writing has consistent slant.
☐ My writing is easy to read.
Circle your best letter on this page.

Hint Overcurves should be rounded.

n m

Think About It You must lift your pencil while writing **K** and **H**. After the lift, start the second stroke close by so that all lines in the letter connect. However, don't place it so close that the letter is cramped.

Begin at the dot. **K** and **H** join the letter that follows.

K   K   Kl   Ko   Kn
K   K   Kl   Ko   Kn

1. Curve forward; slant. Lift.
2. Doublecurve.
3. Curve forward and down; undercurve.

H   H   He   Ha   Hy
H   H   He   Ha   Hy

1. Curve forward; slant. Lift.
2. Curve back; slant.
3. Retrace; loop; curve right.

Hungary King Kong Hyde
Hungary King Kong Hyde

Write on notebook lines. Pages 4–5 will help you.

Helen Keller's story inspires me.
Having no sight or hearing, Keller
became an author and activist.
Helen Keller's story inspired me.
Having no sight or hearing, Keller
became an author and activist

Check Yourself

☐ My letter **K** has no loops.
☐ My letter **H** has a small, open loop.
☐ My writing is easy to read.
Circle your best word on this page.

Hint All strokes in your letters should connect.

K H   **not**   K H

Think About It Look at these letters. They are the same except for their final strokes. In both, make the center undercurve tall and retrace it carefully.

Begin at the dot. **U** and **Y** join the letter that follows.

1. Curve forward; slant; undercurve.
2. Slant; undercurve.

U *U* *Up* *Ug* *Um*
U *U* *Up* *Ug* *Um*

1. Curve forward; slant; undercurve.
2. Slant; loop back; overcurve.

Y *Y* *Yu* *Yo* *Yv*
Y *Y* *Yu* *Yo* *Yv*

Yvonne Ukraine Yoder Ute
Yvonne Ukraine Yoder Ute

Write on notebook lines. Tall letters should not touch the headline.

Under a tree at Yellowstone, Uma and Ursula read A Year Down Yonder. Yolanda took a nap.

Under a tree at Yellowstone, Uma and Ursula read A Year Down Yonder. Yolanda took a nap.

Hint Cross **Y** at the baseline with an overcurve stroke.

Y

Cursive Writing

Think About It   These letters begin with a curve forward stroke. Like **J** and **Y**, **Z** crosses at the baseline with an overcurve. **V** is skinnier than **U,** and ends at the top.

Begin at the dot. **Z** joins the letter that follows. **V** does not.

1. Curve forward and down; slant.
2. Overcurve; curve down; loop; overcurve.

Z   Z   Z   Zu   Za   Zy
Z   Z   Zu   Za   Zy

1. Curve forward; slant; undercurve; overcurve.

V   V   V   Vermont
V   V   V   Vermont

Zimbabwe   Valentine's Day
Zimbabwe   Valentine's Day

Write on notebook lines. Short letters are half the height of tall letters.

Zoey bought a Zippy Tours ticket.
The Vietnam Veterans Memorial was
the tour's first stop.
Zoey bought a Zippy Tours ticket
The Vietnam Veterans Memorial was
the tour's first stop.

Check Yourself

❑ My letter **Z** crosses at the baseline.
❑ I used good spacing between letters, words, and sentences.
❑ My writing is easy to read.
Circle your best word on this page.

Hint   For a legible letter **Z**, pause before writing the first overcurve.

Pause →   *Z*   **not**   *z*

Think About It Look at these letters. They are written with smooth curves. Lift your pencil and cross **X** at the center with a long slant stroke. Be careful when retracing the center stroke of **W**.

Begin at the dot. **W** does not join the letter that follows. Joining **X** is optional.

X   *X*   *X*   *X*   *Xiang*

1. Curve forward; slant; undercurve. Lift.
2. Slant.

X   *X*   *X*   *Xiang*

W   *W*   *W*   *Williams*

1. Curve forward; slant; undercurve.
2. Slant; undercurve; overcurve.

W   *W*   *W*   *Williams*

Xochimilco   *Wednesday*

Xochimilco   *Wednesday*

Write on notebook lines. Pages 4–5 will help you.

Where is Winnie's map? It marked Waterfront Park and Xavier's Cafe with an X.

Hint **X** may join the letter that follows, or not. It's up to you.

Xe   *Xe*

Think About It   Look at these letters. They both have ovals. Both begin with undercurve, slant, retrace. Practice this motion several times on scrap paper.

Begin at the dot. **R** joins the letter that follows. **P** does not.

1. Undercurve.
2. Slant.
3. Retrace; curve forward and back.

P P P P Portugal

P P P Portugal

1. Undercurve.
2. Slant.
3. Retrace; curve forward and back.
4. Curve forward; undercurve.

R R Rh Ra Ry

R R Rh Ra Ry

Pablo Picasso   Paul Revere

Pablo Picasso   Paul Revere

Write on notebook lines. Tall letters should not touch the headline.

Pittsburgh, Pennsylvania, is found at the confluence of the Allegheny River and the Monongahela River.

Check Yourself

☐ My letters **P** and **R** have open ovals.
☐ My short letters are half the height of my tall letters.
☐ My writing is easy to read.

Circle your best word on this page.

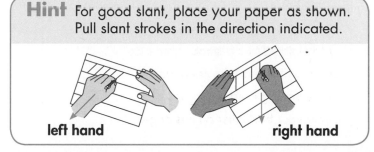

Hint For good slant, place your paper as shown. Pull slant strokes in the direction indicated.

left hand   right hand

Think About It The letter **B** is used frequently, yet it can be tricky to write. Take time to practice the small loop and ending curve right stroke.

Begin at the dot. Joining **B** to the letter that follows is optional.

B *B* *B* *Bahamas*

B *B* *B* *Bahamas*

1. Undercurve.
2. Slant.
3. Retrace; curve forward; loop; curve forward and back.
4. Retrace; curve right.

Black Beauty *Botswana*

Black Beauty *Botswana*

Barbara Bush *Barbados*

Barbara Bush *Barbados*

Write on notebook lines. Short letters are half the height of tall letters.

Both bright students, sisters Elizabeth Blackwell and Emily Blackwell were among the first female doctors.

Check Yourself

☐ My letter **B** has a small, open loop.
☐ My writing has consistent slant.
☐ My writing is easy to read.
Circle your best letter on this page.

Hint Do you prefer to join **B** to other letters, or not? It's up to you.

Brazil *Brazil*

Think About It   These letters are nearly identical. Finish **F** with a slide right stroke at the center so it is not mistaken for **T**. Practice the doublecurve stroke on scrap paper.

Begin at the dot. Joining **T** and **F** to the letter that follows is optional.

$\mathcal{T}$ $\mathcal{T}$ $\mathcal{T}$ $\mathcal{T}$ $\mathcal{T}$ *Tuesday*

1. Slant.
2. Curve forward and right. Lift.
3. Doublecurve; curve up.
4. Retrace; curve right.

$\mathcal{F}$ $\mathcal{F}$ $\mathcal{F}$ $\mathcal{F}$ $\mathcal{F}$ *Franklin*

1. Slant.
2. Curve forward and right. Lift.
3. Doublecurve; curve up.
4. Retrace; curve right. Lift.
5. Slide right.

Fiji   Trinidad and Tobago

Write on notebook lines. Pages 4–5 will help you.

From an early age, Henry Ford tinkered with motors. The 1908 Ford Model T was a huge success.

Check *Yourself*

❏ My letters **T** and **F** have good shape.
❏ My uppercase letters are tall.
❏ My writing is easy to read.
Circle your best word on this page.

Hint   You decide whether to join **T** and **F** to the letter that follows.

Th   Th
Fr   Fr

Think About It Look at these letters. They share unusual loops and a final retrace, curve right stroke. **G** will be easy to read when it has a sharp "point" at the top right. **S** will be easy to read when its bottom loop is largest.

Begin at the dot. Joining **G** and **S** to the letter that follows is optional.

G G G G Godzilla

1. Undercurve; loop; curve forward.
2. Doublecurve; curve up.
3. Retrace; curve right.

S S S S Saturday

1. Undercurve; loop; curve down and up.
2. Retrace; curve right.

Theodor Seuss Geisel

Write on notebook lines. Tall letters should not touch the headline.

Gayle Green's favorite picture book is The Giving Tree. Shel Silverstein is the author.

Check Yourself

☐ My loops are open in **G** and **S**.
☐ My writing has consistent slant.
☐ My writing is easy to read.
Circle your best letter on this page.

Hint Decide whether you prefer to join **G** and **S** to the letter that follows.

Go Go

See See

Think About It Look at these letters. Each one has two small loops. For legibility, make sure to keep the loops open. Notice that **L**'s last stroke dips below the baseline.

Begin at the dot. **L** and **D** do not join the letter that follows.

L   *L*   *L*   *L*   *Lincoln*

1. Undercurve; loop; curve down; loop; curve under.

D   *D*   *D*   *D*   *Diego*

1. Downcurve; loop; curve down and up; loop; curve right.

Labor Day   Dr.   London

Write on notebook lines. Short letters are half the height of tall letters.

Lindsay learned that the Miami Dolphins and the Detroit Lions are two teams in the N F L.

Check *Yourself*

❏ My letter **L** is written with one smooth line.
❏ My letter **D** touches the baseline in two places.
❏ My writing is easy to read.
Circle your best word on this page.

Hint Without good loops, **L** may look like **Z** and **D** may look like **O**.

L D   not   *L D*

Uppercase Joinings

As you have learned, some uppercase letters always join to the letter that follows. Others never join. For a third set of uppercase letters, the choice to join or not is up to you.

Uppercase Letters That Always Join:

Uppercase Letters That Never Join:

Uppercase Letters With Optional Joinings:

Take a look at these hints for uppercase letters that join.

Undercurve Joinings

Undercurve-to-Undercurve

Swing wide to form undercurve of next letter.

Undercurve-to-Downcurve

Swing over to form top of downcurve letter.

Undercurve-to-Overcurve

Swing up and over. Undercurve turns into overcurve.

Overcurve Joinings

Overcurve-to-Undercurve

Swing up across the baseline and into the undercurve of the next letter.

Overcurve-to-Downcurve

Overcurve swings up across the baseline and becomes top of downcurve letter.

Overcurve-to-Overcurve

Overcurve swings up across baseline and curves over into top of next letter.

Write the names of world capitals. Join uppercase letters correctly.

Kabul, Afghanistan

Zagreb, Croatia

Cairo, Egypt

Rabat, Morocco

Yaren, Nauru

Kiev, Ukraine

Tokyo, Japan

Havana, Cuba

Check Yourself

❐ My letters and joining strokes have good **shape**.

❐ My letters are the correct **size**.

❐ My writing has consistent **slant**.

❐ Good joining strokes make good **spacing** between my letters.

❐ My writing is easy to read.

Common Problems and Corrective Strategies

Pay attention to these common problems that can make cursive writing illegible. Use the corrective strategies to write each letter legibly.

Problem Letters have unnecessary loops.

U H B W

Corrective Strategy Pause before the retrace. Retrace lines smoothly and carefully.

U H B W

Problem Ending strokes have poor shape.

n v y z

Corrective Strategy Study the model letters, arrows, and stroke descriptions. Use good basic strokes when writing letters.

n v y z

Problem Strokes do not connect.

R K a D

Corrective Strategy Make sure to complete each stroke when writing a letter. Touch your pencil to previously written strokes to make sure strokes connect.

R K a D

Problem Slant is poor.

X C E S

Corrective Strategy Position your paper for writing as shown on page 35. Pull strokes in the direction indicated. Cursive writing should have a consistent, forward slant.

X C E S

Problem Loops are too large or too small.

I G J P

Corrective Strategy Keep loops open, but don't let them get too fat. Writing letters with good shape will come with practice and evaluation.

I G J P

Problem Strokes overlap.

T F

Corrective Strategy After the lift, place pencil on curve forward stroke before beginning the doublecurve stroke.

T F

Write the names of famous American streets and roads. Avoid common errors.

Pennsylvania Avenue

Lombard Street

U.S. Route 66

Blue Ridge Parkway

Park Avenue   Wall Street

Writing for Tests

Legibility is important when you write for a test. Sometimes you will write responses on a classroom exam. Other times you will write essays on a standardized test that will be scored by outside evaluators. Research shows that people who grade tests are more likely to award higher scores to papers with neat, legible handwriting.

If you are like most people, you feel the pressure of time when you take a test. On a test, your handwriting needs to be speedy and easy to read. Is that possible? Yes!

Read the test question and the first three sentences of a student's response. On the lines below, write the sentences legibly, at your usual pace.

Directions: Write a narrative essay about a time you changed your mind about something important.

Luis lives on my street. We weren't always friends. I'd known him since kindergarten, so I thought I knew everything about him.

Write the sentences again. This time, write more quickly. Make sure your writing is still legible.

This time when you write the sentences, time yourself. You should be able to write them legibly in about a minute.

_____

_____

_____

_____

Now, write the beginning of your own response to the test question. Take some time to plan what you will write. As you write, don't think too much about handwriting. Let it flow naturally while you concentrate on the content of your writing. Write for one minute.

_____

_____

_____

_____

_____

_____

_____

_____

Check Yourself

☐ Each letter is easy to read because it has good **shape**.

☐ My short letters are half the **size** of my tall letters.

☐ My **slant** is consistent, giving an overall neat appearance.

☐ There is good **spacing** between letters, words, and sentences.

☐ My writing is easy to read.

Cursive Review

Write the names of festivals and holidays from around the world. Before you begin, review the
Keys to Legibility for Cursive Writing on pages 34–35.

May Day –England

Children's Day –Turkey

Cinco de Mayo –Mexico

Esala Perahera –Sri Lanka

Chinese New Year –China

Raksha Bandhan –India

Day of the Dead –Ecuador

Carnival – Brazil

Thanksgiving – Canada

Trung Thu – Vietnam

Doll's Festival – Japan

St. Lucia – Sweden

N'cwala – Zambia

Write two sentences about your favorite holiday or festival. Avoid common errors.

Check Yourself

❏ My letters have good **shape**.

❏ My letters are the correct **size**.

❏ The **slant** of my writing is consistent.

❏ I used good **spacing** between letters, words, and sentences.

❏ My writing is easy to read.

Cursive Posttest

Write the riddles in your best cursive handwriting. As you write, remember the **Keys to Legibility** explained on pages 34–35.

What can run but never walks, has a mouth but never talks, has a head but never weeps, and has a bed but never sleeps? A river!

_____

_____

_____

_____

Johnny's mother had four children. The first was April, the second was May, and the third was June. What was the name of her fourth child? Johnny!

_____

_____

_____

_____

What goes around the world and stays in a corner? A stamp!

_____

_____

_____

_____

Check Yourself

❏ My letters have good **shape**.

❏ My letters are the correct **size**.

❏ My writing has consistent **slant**.

❏ I used good **spacing** between letters, words, and sentences.

❏ My writing is easy to read.